JOSEPH MIDTHUN   SAMUEL HITI

BUILDING BLOCKS OF SCIENCE

THE RESPIRATORY SYSTEM

WORLD BOOK

a Scott Fetzer company
Chicago
www.worldbook.com

World Book, Inc.
233 N. Michigan Avenue
Chicago, IL 60601
U.S.A.

For information about other World Book publications,
visit our website at www.worldbook.com
or call 1-800-WORLDBK (967-5325).
For information about sales to schools and libraries,
call 1-800-975-3250 (United States),
or 1-800-837-5365 (Canada).

Library of Congress Cataloging-in-Publication Data

The respiratory system.
    pages cm. -- (Building blocks of science)
    Summary: "A graphic nonfiction volume that
introduces the respiratory system in the human
body"-- Provided by publisher.
    Includes index.
    ISBN 978-0-7166-1847-8
    1. Respiratory organs--Juvenile literature.
2. Respiratory organs--Diseases--Juvenile
literature. 3. Respiration--Juvenile literature.
4. Respiratory organs--Comic books, strips, etc.
5. Respiratory organs--Diseases--Comic books,
strips, etc. 6. Respiration--Comic books, strips,
etc. 7. Graphic novels. I. World Book, Inc.
QP121.R466 2014
612.2--dc23
                        2013024692

Building Blocks of Science
ISBN: 978-0-7166-1840-9 (set, hc.)

Printed in China by Shenzhen Donnelley
Printing Co., Ltd., Guangdong Province
1st printing October 2013

Acknowledgments:
Created by Samuel Hiti and Joseph Midthun
Art by Samuel Hiti
Written by Joseph Midthun
Special thanks to Syril McNally

TABLE OF CONTENTS

There is a glossary on page 30. Terms defined in the glossary are in type **that looks like this** on their first appearance.

Several **organs** and muscles make up the respiratory system.

The nose and mouth connect to a large tube called the **trachea,** or windpipe.

The trachea begins at the back of the mouth, runs down the neck into the upper chest, and splits into two smaller tubes...

...called **bronchi.**

Each of these tubes leads to the lungs.

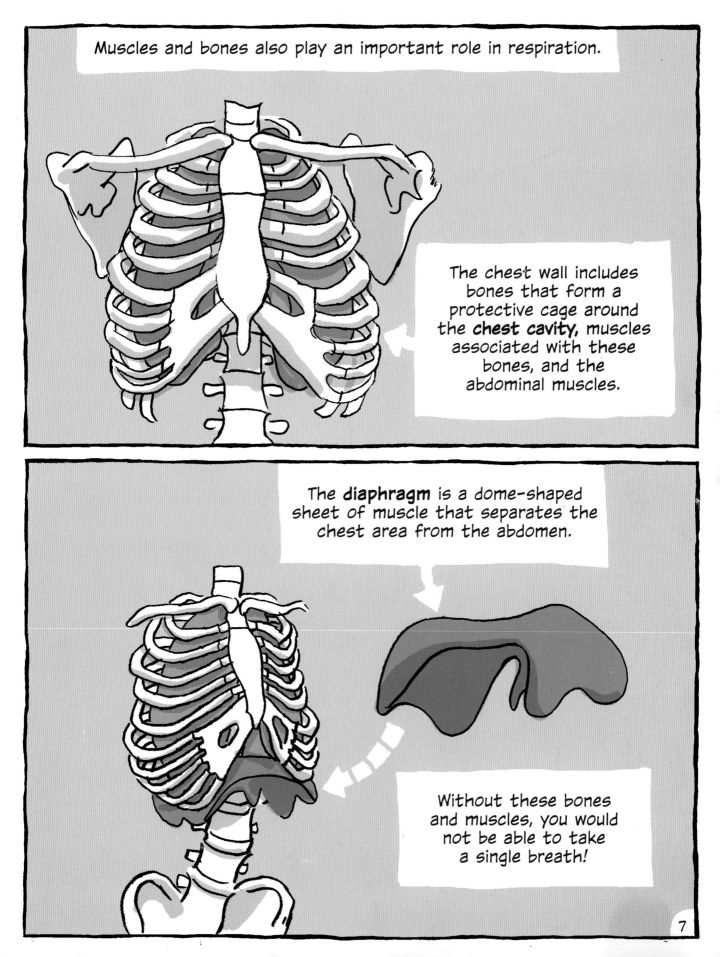

Muscles and bones also play an important role in respiration.

The chest wall includes bones that form a protective cage around the **chest cavity,** muscles associated with these bones, and the abdominal muscles.

The **diaphragm** is a dome-shaped sheet of muscle that separates the chest area from the abdomen.

Without these bones and muscles, you would not be able to take a single breath!

INHALATION AND EXHALATION

Breathing consists of two acts: breathing in, or **inhalation**...

...and breathing out, or **exhalation**.

When you inhale, the diaphragm and the muscles of the chest wall contract.

This action lifts the ribs and makes the chest cavity longer and wider, causing the lungs to expand and draw in air.

The lower parts of each lung contain elastic fibers in the walls of the airways.

When you inhale and the lungs expand, these elastic **tissues** stretch—

—like an inflating balloon.

When you exhale, the diaphragm and the rib muscles relax.

The elastic tissues of the lung shrink, pulling the walls of the rib cage with them.

This shrinking of the lungs pushes air out of the body—

—like a deflating balloon!

Sqeep

When you finish exhaling, the process starts over again!

But that's not all that happens when you breathe!

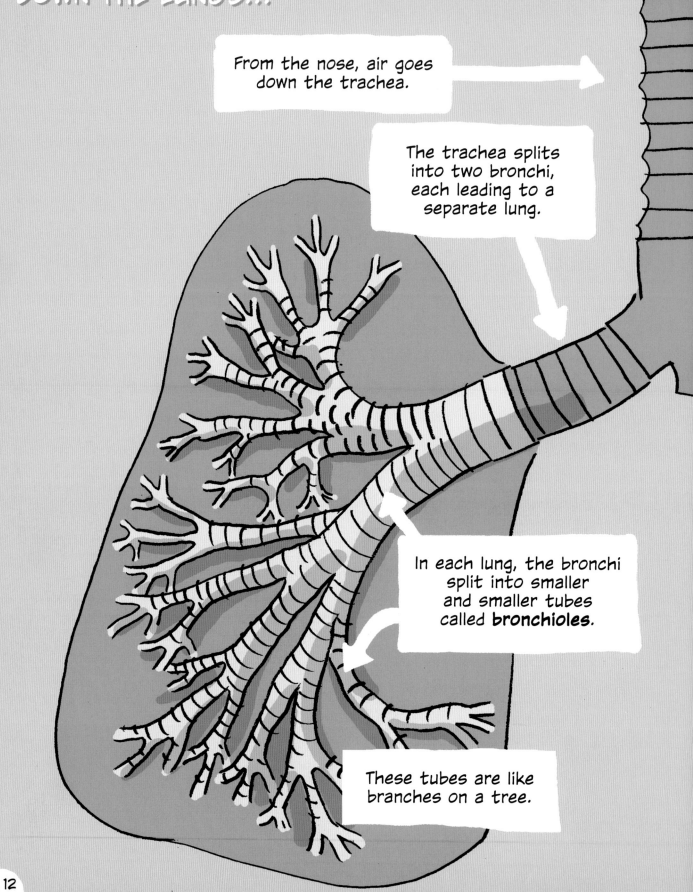

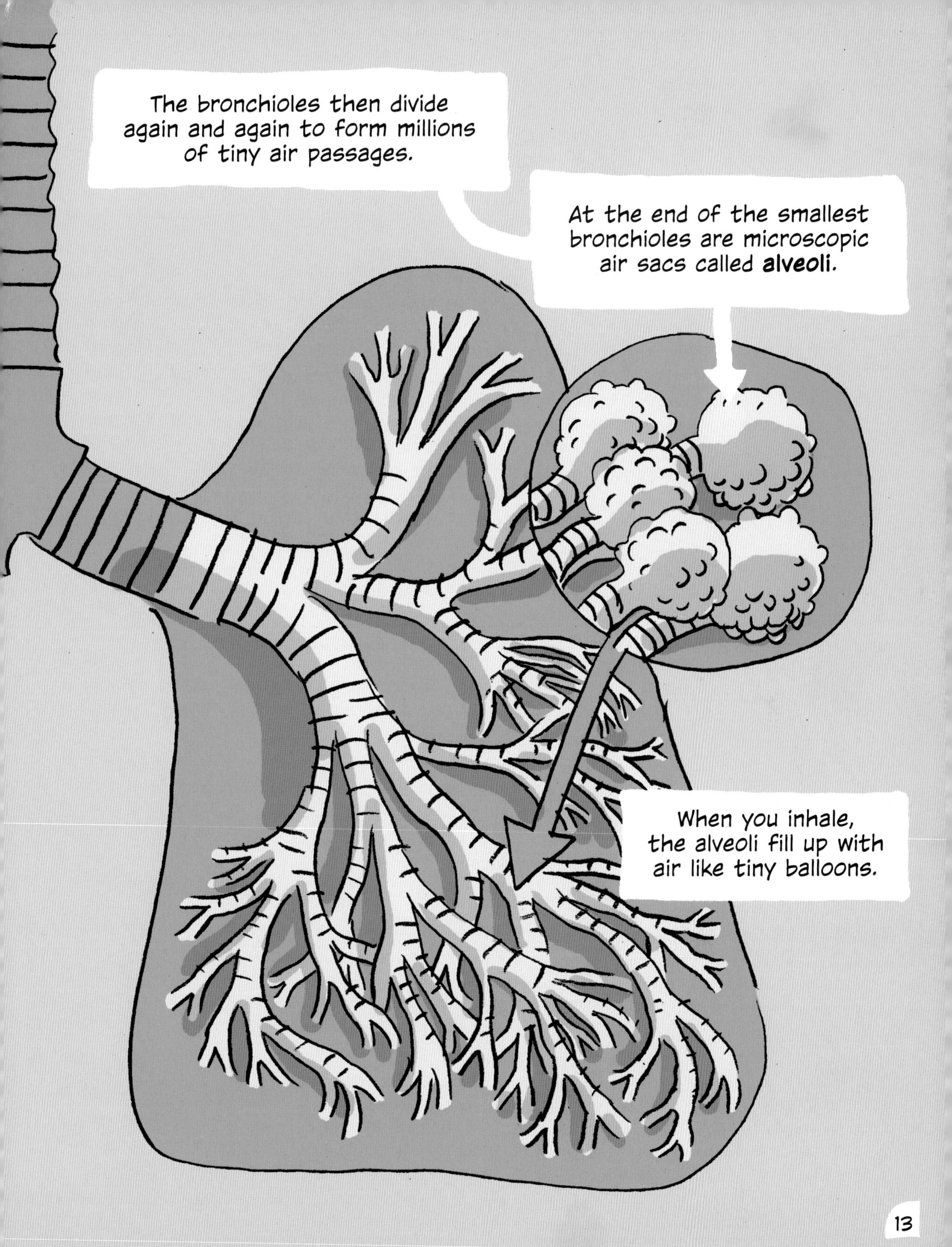
The bronchioles then divide again and again to form millions of tiny air passages.
At the end of the smallest bronchioles are microscopic air sacs called **alveoli**.
When you inhale, the alveoli fill up with air like tiny balloons.

Through the power of the circulatory system, oxygen is transported to your cells by your heart and blood.

At the same time, waste gases like carbon dioxide pass from the cells into the blood...

...and back to the lungs.

The waste gases are then transferred through the capillaries into your alveoli...

...and back out of your nose or mouth.

Exhalation!

Altitude, or height, can also affect the respiratory system.

Oxygen makes up 21 percent of the air.

At sea level, there is more than enough oxygen for humans to breathe easily.

But at higher altitudes, air is thinner.

Mount Everest is the tallest peak above sea level on Earth...

At the top, about 9,000 meters, there is only a fourth as much oxygen as there is at sea level!

Very few people can survive the climb to the top of Everest without breathing equipment.

Yet, some people live at heights of about 3,900 meters above sea level, and most humans can get used to living at this height.

You are surrounded by germs, and sometimes they get into your nose, mouth, and throat.

And when we get in, we'll make you sick!

Your body tries to kick out these invaders. The lining of your nose becomes inflamed and produces large amounts of mucus to flush out the germs. That's why your nose gets stuffy.

The cause of these symptoms is often a tiny **virus**—a germ even smaller than bacteria.

wipe

About 200 different kinds of virus are known to cause colds.

Even when you are healthy, your body works to prevent dust and germs from getting inside.

When something irritates your nose or throat, you cough—or sneeze.

cough cough

When you cough, your stomach and diaphragm muscles contract suddenly...

STOMACH

DIAPHRAGM

...sending a high-speed jet of air up your throat and out of your mouth.

A sneeze is similar to a cough, but the air goes out through the nose rather than the mouth.

AH-CHOO!

When germs do get past the nose, your lungs have special defenses to kick them out and keep you from getting sick.

Just like your nose, the lungs contain cilia that move back and forth, gradually pushing any particles trapped in the mucus up and out of the trachea.

Pneumonia is an infection of the lungs often caused by bacteria.

When you have pneumonia, your lung tissues become inflamed.

Luckily, modern **antibiotics** can kill bacteria in the lungs.

The best way to prevent yourself from getting these bacteria is to wash your hands regularly.

Scrub Scrub

SOAP

People with **asthma** suffer from inflammation of the bronchi, which obstructs airflow.

You okay?

GASP.

When someone has an asthma attack, they can use medicines that decrease constriction in the airways.

These medicines relax small muscles in and around the lungs.

GLOSSARY

allergy a bodily reaction to a particular substance.

alveoli tiny air sacs in the lungs.

antibiotics useful medications for treating infections caused by bacteria.

asthma a condition that makes breathing difficult and causes coughing.

bacterium; bacteria a tiny single-celled organism; more than one bacterium.

blood vessel a hollow tube that carries blood and nutrients through the body.

bronchi airways to the lungs.

bronchiole a small tube that branches off the bronchi.

capillary a blood vessel with a very narrow opening.

carbon dioxide the air that is breathed out of the lungs.

cell the basic unit of all living things.

chest cavity the hollow space between the neck and the abdomen. The chest cavity is enclosed by the ribs.

cilia tiny, hairlike structures that line the nose.

diaphragm a muscular sheet that separates the chest cavity from the abdomen.

exhalation breathing out.

inhalation breathing in.

microbe tiny organism, such as a bacterium or virus, that can cause disease.

organ two or more tissues that work together to do a certain job.

respiration the process by which organisms get and use oxygen.

respiratory system the group of organs that brings oxygen into the body and removes carbon dioxide.

tissue a group of similar cells that do a certain job.

trachea a long tube by which air is carried to and from the lungs.

virus a tiny germ that causes certain infections.

FIND OUT MORE

Books

How Do Your Lungs Work?
Don L. Curry
(Children's Press, 2004)

Human Body
by Richard Walker
(DK Children, 2009)

Human Body Factory: The Nuts and Bolts of Your Insides
by Dan Green
(Kingfisher, 2012)

Lungs: Your Respiratory System
by Seymour Simon
(HarperCollins, 2007)

Start Exploring: Gray's Anatomy: A Fact-Filled Coloring Book
by Freddy Stark
(Running Press Kids, 2011)

The Lungs and Breathing
by Carol Ballard
(KidHaven, 2005)

The Remarkable Respiratory System: How Do My Lungs Work?
by John Burstein
(Crabtree, 2009)

The Respiratory System
by Christine Taylor-Butler
(Children's Press, 2008)

The Way We Work
by David Macaulay
(Houghton Mifflin/Walter Lorraine Books, 2008)

Websites

Allergy Learning Games For Kids
http://www.learninggamesforkids.com/health_games_allergies.html
Learn about allergies with a word definition matching quiz and other fun games that blend life science with other skills.

Biology 4 Kids: Respiratory System
http://www.biology4kids.com/files/systems_respiratory.html
Get an in-depth education on all of the parts that make up the respiratory system.

E-Learning for Kids: The Respiratory System
http://www.e-learningforkids.org/Courses/Liquid_Animation/Body_Parts/Respiratory_System/
Take a peek inside your respiratory system in this clickable lesson with bonus comprehension exercises.

Kids Biology: Respiratory System
http://www.kidsbiology.com/human_biology/respiratory-system.php
Learn all about the respiratory system by watching a short video and reading fact-filled articles complete with images of the body's organs.

Kids Health: How the Body Works
http://kidshealth.org/kid/htbw/
Select a body part to watch a video, play a word find, or read an article to learn more about its function in the human body.

NeoK12: Respiratory System
http://www.neok12.com/Respiratory-System.htm
Watch videos that illustrate the flow of the respiratory system, and then take grade-specific quizzes to test your knowledge.

Science Kids: Human Body for Kids
http://www.sciencekids.co.nz/humanbody.html
Sample a range of educational games, challenging experiments, and mind-bending quizzes all while learning about human body topics.

INDEX